From

The Women's Press Ltd
34 Great Sutton Street, London EC1V 0DX

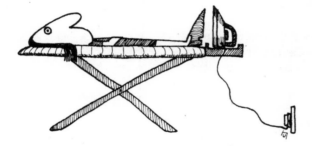

Cath Jackson lives and works in North London. She likes peanut butter sandwiches and opera and her main ambition is to retire to a tweed skirt in the country and grow dogs.

Visibly Vera

Cartoons by
Cath Jackson

 The Women's Press

First published by The Women's Press Ltd 1986
A member of the Namara Group
34 Great Sutton Street, London EC1V 0DX

British Library Cataloguing in Publication Data

Jackson, Cath
    Visibly Vera.
    1. English wit and humor, Pictorial
    I. Title
    741.5'942   NC1479

    ISBN 0-7043-4029-1

Printed and bound in Great Britain
by Nene Litho and Woolnough Bookbinding
both of Wellingborough, Northants

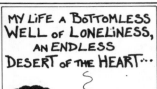

"Dynamic Go-getting Executive Team seeks Bright Energetic Girl Friday······ Relaxed, friendly Atmosphere······ Exciting new opportunities···

Phase One

Phase Two

Phase Three

Phase Four

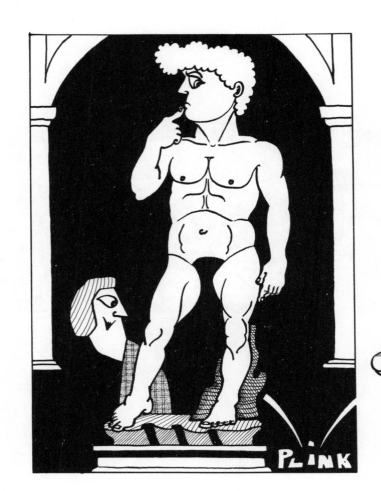

A Good Bitch
Cartoons by Angela Martin

The bitch strikes back! A feast of cartoons about dogs, people, archangels and other species. Angela Martin chews life up with relish and drops it back at our feet with a wicked grin…or is it a snarl?

0 7043 3956 0
£1.99